This Book
Belongs to:

_____

Published in the United States
by ArtisticWill Designs
www.artisticwilldesigns.com
Trade Paperback ISBN 978-0-9994803-0-4
Printed in the United States of America

ArtisticWill Designs
Joyce Yoshihara Will
artisticwilldesigns.com

Color Test page:

Sample your markers, gel pens, and pencils on this practice page.

Coloring Tips:

1) Remember to place a sheet of cardboard behind each page you are going to color. This helps prevent indentation marks or ink bleeding through to the page below. Wet mediums, such as gel pens and markers, may bleed through the paper. Dry mediums, such as colored pencils, can create pleasing results.

2) Illustrations of fabric, foliage, and patterns can be colored with either one color or a variety of colors. Remember, many Japanese patterns are embossed or etched into the fabric with one color, while other fabrics have many colored details. Don't let the details scare you; it is not necessary to color every section that is drawn.

3) In the right corner, a Japanese "Hanko" signature is stamped and is usually one color, such as red or gold. You don't have to be concerned about the fine details of this stamp.

ArtisticWill Designs

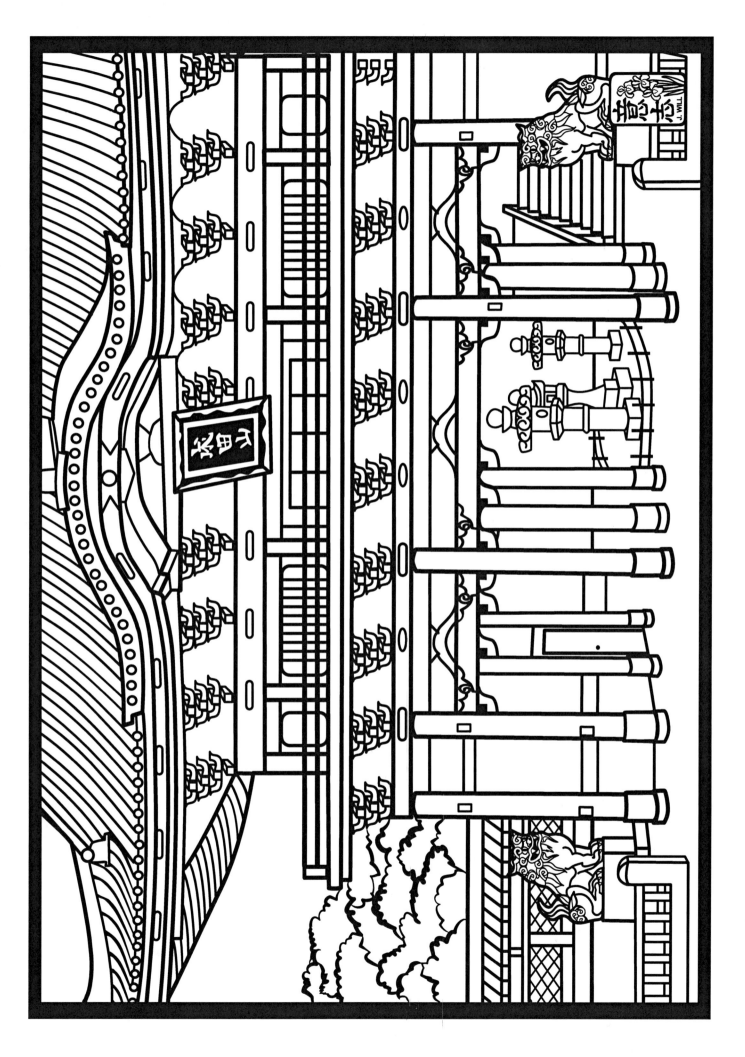

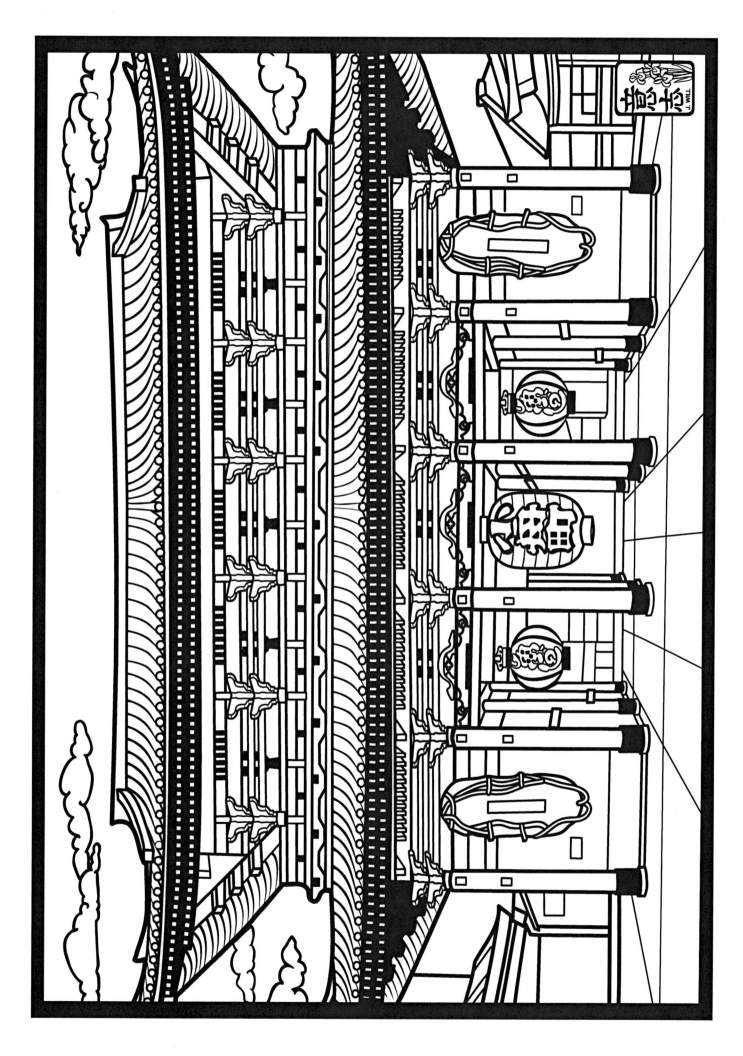

意志

J. WILL

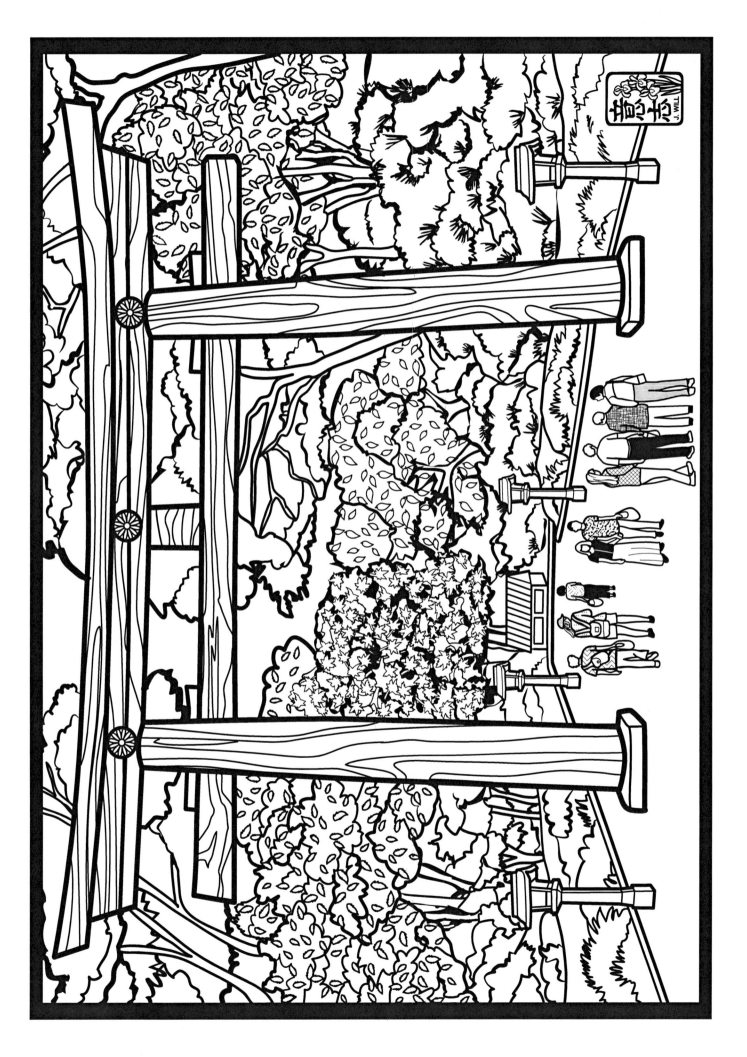

意志

J. WILL

意志

J. WILL

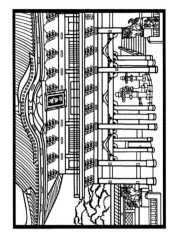

Narita-san Gateway:
A massive gateway stands in front of a beautiful Shinsho-ji Buddhist Temple, built in 940 A.D. It's a short walk from Narita International airport near Tokyo. Lush gardens, decorative ponds filled with koi fish, and a three-story pagoda surround the temple, which attracts a large number of worshipers and visitors throughout the year.

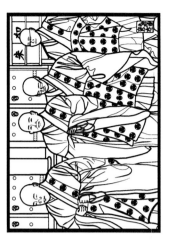

Buddhist Monks:
Religion is an integral part of Japan's culture. Many Japanese people practice both Buddhist and Shinto traditions. Buddhism includes the beliefs of enlightenment, reincarnation, and the after life. The Buddhist priests usually perform funerals, while Shinto priests are in high demand for weddings.

Kimono Style Patterns:
Many Japanese design elements are taken from nature, such as flowers and butterflies. Other designs are graphic or modern. Depending on the use, these can be painted, silk screened, or woven into intricate designs. Some Japanese designs are seen on origami paper, handkerchiefs, or decorative patterns.

Narita-san Temple, Decorative Ceiling Tiles:
The interior of Narita-san temple is filled with intricate carvings and lavishly decorated ceiling tiles. All the decor is designed for aesthetics, beauty, and meditation.

Narita-san Temple, Pagoda:
Standing in front of Narita-san's main temple is an 18th century three-story pagoda that is covered with intricate carvings of golden dragons and swirls of colors representing clouds and the wind.

Narita-san Temple Garden:
Japanese gardens reflect the essence of nature for zen meditation, tranquility, and enlightenment. Many gardens contain stone lanterns, koi ponds, manicured trees, and stylized landscapes which resemble nature.

Robots:
Japan has a fascination with robotics and they have become the leader in robotic technology. These particular robots have sensors which allow them to detect movements and speak short phrases. They also have motorized wheels to help them move around.

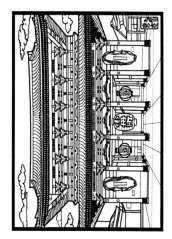

Kaminari-mon Gateway, Asakusa:
This Buddhist gateway is called the Kaminari-mon or Thunder Gate. It holds giant paper lanterns to welcome visiting worshipers and guests. On one side of the gateway is a shopping district called Nakamise-dori with two rows of vendors selling traditional crafts and souvenirs. On the other side of the Gateway is the entrance to the Sensho-ji Buddhist temple.

Seno-ji Temple, Asakusa:
It is known as the oldest Buddhist temple, founded in 628 A.D. to house the deity Mercy Kannon. Buddhism was restricted for thousands of years before World War II, when the Emperor lifted the restriction. Thousands of visitors now come to this sacred place of worship.

Koi Pond:
Koi, a type of carp fish, are very popular in Japan. They are symbols of good luck and are can be found throughout the country. Koi ponds are seen in front of tea houses and near manicured gardens.

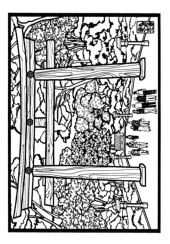

Meiji-jingu Shinto Shrine:
A giant 40 ft tall Tori gate stands in front of the famous Meiji-jingu Shinto shrine. Tori gates mark the threshold of a sacred place. This Tori gate is made from Cypress wood and is the largest Tori gate in Japan. The Shinto shrine is surrounded by 175 acres of manicured gardens and has two other large Tori gates.

Folding Fans:
Japan has very humid summers and many people use folding fans to keep themselves cool when the temperature rises. The fans are covered with washi paper with beautiful designs or simple patterns. The folding ribs of the fans are made from bamboo, and some are painted with black lacquer for elegance and beauty.

Imperial Palace:
The emperor and the royal family live in the Imperial Palace. It is closed to the public, but is open to visitors twice a year on the Emperor's birthday and New Years. A moat and two arched stone bridges surround this beautiful structure. Outside the palace are guard towers, a museum, manicured gardens, and public parks.

Koinobori Flags:
Koi streamers are flown all over Japan on May 5th to celebrate "Boys' Day." These flags are symbols of blessings for healthy children. Brightly colored Koi streamers are raised on poles so that air can blow through the front of their open mouths.

Maneki Neko:
Called a beckoning cat, they are believed to bring good luck. There are many colors: white, gold, pink, red, green, and black. Some beckoning cats represent luck in happiness, romance, health, education, and money. The left paw up invites customers to businesses or guests to homes. The right paw up invites good fortune.

Mt Fuji 5th Station:
Mt Fuji has 10 levels, called stations, leading up to the peak. Most visitors start their hike at the 5th station near rest areas and gifts shops. The 7th and 8th stations have lodging for tired and sleepy hikers. In the past, it was considered a sacred mountain and only priests were allowed to climb it. Now hikers of all levels and ages climb beloved Mt Fuji.

Mt Fuji:
Mt Fuji is a great symbol of Japan. It also has the distinguished title of "Unesco World Heritage Site." It is a volcano that has been dormant since 1707 and is the highest mountain in Japan, standing at 12,390 ft. Mt Fuji has been represented on artwork, block prints, motifs, and decorative designs.

Ryokan Inn:
Traditional guesthouse inns have special accommodations for their guests. Rooms are furnished with tatami straw mats, shoji rice paper screens, simple decor, and soft quilted futon bedding. The inn provides a lightweight kimono called a yukata. Ryokan have natural mineral hot spring baths called Onsen for their visitors to relax and unwind in.

Matsumoto Castle:
A military fort used during the Shogun era. It's the oldest castle, dating back to 1593 A.D. It was designed for defense with archers' nooks, portholes for shooting guns, and areas for soldiers to drop stones on their enemies. The beautiful five-tier castle is surrounded by a moat and high stone walls. The top tier contains a shrine to the "Goddess of the 26th night", for protection from invasion.

Samurai Warriors:
During the Edo period, samurai warriors were members of the military who wore protective armor. Each clan was identified with different armor colors, motifs, and colorful waving banners. Because the last Shogun ruler wanted to protect against any hostile takeover, he destroyed hundreds of castles throughout Japan. Only a handful of these castles remain today.

Fighting Samurai Frogs:
A short walk from Matsumoto Castle is a strange statue that welcomes visitors to the shopping district. You'll find a giant statue of two samurai frogs fighting against a massive toad. They are dressed in kimonos and have their katana swords drawn ready for the attack. Frogs are good luck symbols in Matsumoto Prefecture.

Tamari String Balls:
A traditional craft utilizing rolled scraps of kimono fabric and colorful threads. The threads are wrapped and woven around the fabric to create balls with intricate patterns and designs. This craft is done by the dedicated local craftsmen.

Manhole Drain Cover, Tamari String Balls:
Each prefecture in Japan has stylized drain covers repesenting an element that is important to that area. Many are used for electricity, water, and drainage excess for the streets.

Traditional Homes:
Traditional Japanese homes had a living quarters with a sunken fire pit for heating and preparing meals. Rooms had tatami straw mats, sliding shoji rice paper screens, and nooks for storing quilted futon bedding. Many tradional homes had an outside garden to promote tranquility while looking at nature.

Sushi:
Steamed white rice is flavored with a vinegar mixture and then rolled, filled, or topped with raw seafood and vegetables. Wasabi, a green condiment similar to horse radish with a spicy flavor, is added to the sushi to enhance the flavor of the raw seafood. It is also used to help prevent an upset stomach from eating raw fish.

Takayama City:
Japan has many well preserverved ancient cities that are scattered throughout the country. Travel back in time by walking through narrow streets lined with wooden buildings serving as inns, restaurants, and shops selling traditional goods. At times, actors will dress in authentic clothing to recall the feeling of a bygone era.

Cherry Blossom Screen:
Cherry blossoms, called Sakura, are one of Japan's sacred flowers, symbolizing beauty and resiliance. Sakura are so popular that many people will camp out for the best viewing spots during blooming season in mid-April. Sakura motifs can be seen on just about everything, including food decorations, clothing designs, furniture, decor, and painted screens.

Shirakawa-go Thatched Roof Houses:
The unique "A" shaped roofs of Shirakawa-go are made of straw bundles stacked three feet deep to protect against heavy snowfall in the winter. The homes are constructed using interlocking wood frames without any nails. Many homes are 3-5 stories tall, and the roofs on the 5-story home can reach up to 30 ft high. The bottom floor is used for shops, the second floor is for living quarters, and the top floors is used for raising silk worms.

Manhole Drain Cover, Shirakawa-go Houses:
Shirakawa-go mountain village has manhole drain grates with the iconic "A" shaped houses and mountainous landscapes, which represent a popular feature in this prefecture.

Wooden Prayer Plaques:
Prayer plaques called "Ema" are seen at Shinto shrines and Buddhist temples. Prayers or wishes are written on these plaques and hung on display. People commonly pray for relationships, health, education, or safe birth. After a period of time, these plaques are burned in a special ceremony to raise the prayers to the heavens.

About:
Hello. I'm Joyce Yoshihara Will, artist and owner of ArtisticWill Designs.
I'm a wife, mom, and artist living in Southern California. Art has always been part of my life. With a BFA in Illustration, I've worked for major companies in the past including Northrop Grumman, Ralph M. Parsons, and Big 5 Sporting Goods. After raising my family, my heart was pulled back toward illustrations.

Heartfelt Thanks:
Deepest gratitude is given to my husband and family for their love and constant support. Thank you to my close friends for their enthusiasm and for being my greatest cheering section. Thank you to my mom and dad for instilling in me a love for Japan's culture and traditions.

Inspiration:
I traveled to Japan to experience the country of my heritage. I was so inspired by Japan's beauty, culture, and people that I had to illustrate its "essence" into a coloring book.

Art:
All illustrations are my personal creations, never using any purchased or royalty free stock images. The art is digitally hand drawn using a Wacom drawing tablet in Adobe Illustrator to create vectored line art. Personal photos are used as reference. Models' faces have been altered to protect their identities. All art is copyrighted.

Released 2018: "Essence of Japan", Volume 2
Destinations: Kyoto, Osaka, Gion, and Nara prefectures.
- Bamboo Forest
- Golden Pavilion
- 1000 Tori Gates
- Todaiji Temple
- Shinto Shrine

ArtisticWill Designs

CPSIA information can be obtained
at www.ICGtesting.com
Printed in the USA
FSOW02n0906140218
44448FS

9 780999 480304